Firefighters Are Friends

Ron Rakosnik

Tampa, Florida

Firefighters Are Friends

Published by Gatekeeper Press
7853 Gunn Hwy, Suite 209
Tampa, FL 33626
www.GatekeeperPress.com

Library of Congress Control Number: 2023939109
ISBN (hardcover): 9781662939433
ISBN (paperback): 9781662939440
eISBN: 9781662939457

This book is dedicated to all first responders—fire and police—past, present, and future.

To those members who teach our citizens, young and old, how to be safe and remain safe with our family and friends in our daily lives.

Introduction

The purpose of the book is to teach our young citizens the importance of being safe and knowing what to do in case of an emergency. We've found that early-childhood safety lessons go a long way as our young citizens grow and get older. I wanted to give back some important safety tips through an enjoyable book for young and old.

I hope the book is a good teaching book, people will learn some safety items, and the book may inspire a young girl or boy to maybe one day become a firefighter.

Jimmy's mom brought him to kindergarten on his first day of school. In kindergarten, Jimmy would make many friends and learn new things.

When school started in September, Jimmy learned his home address, phone number, and the alphabet.

In October, a firefighter visited Jimmy's school.
Firefighter Fred read a story to the class.
He brought his fire boots, fire coat, and helmet.

Firefighter Fred taught
the class to call 9-1-1 if there
is an emergency—at home or
away from home.

He also told the class that it is important to have a family meeting place to go to if there is smoke or a fire in your home.

Firefighter Fred said that every room of the house
should have a working smoke detector. Smoke detectors
beep to warn of smoke or fire.

Remember, if you are away from home—at a park, at the pool, or somewhere else—and you need the fire department or an ambulance, you should call 9-1-1.

When Jimmy arrived home from school, he asked his mom if they could visit the fire station one day. She said, "yes."

Jimmy and his mom visited the fire station,
and they met Firefighter Fred, who gave them a tour.

Firefighter Fred showed them the kitchen
where the firefighters make their lunch and dinner.
Next, they saw the bunk room where
the firefighters sleep overnight.

They visited the exercise room where firefighters
work out to stay strong and healthy. Then, they went
to the classroom where the firefighters
continue to learn about their job.

The fire engine:
Pumps the water
Four firefighters
Fire hose
Finally, Firefighter Fred showed Jimmy and his mom the fire station's garage.

The fire ladder truck:
Carries many ladders and tools
Large ladder to reach higher heights

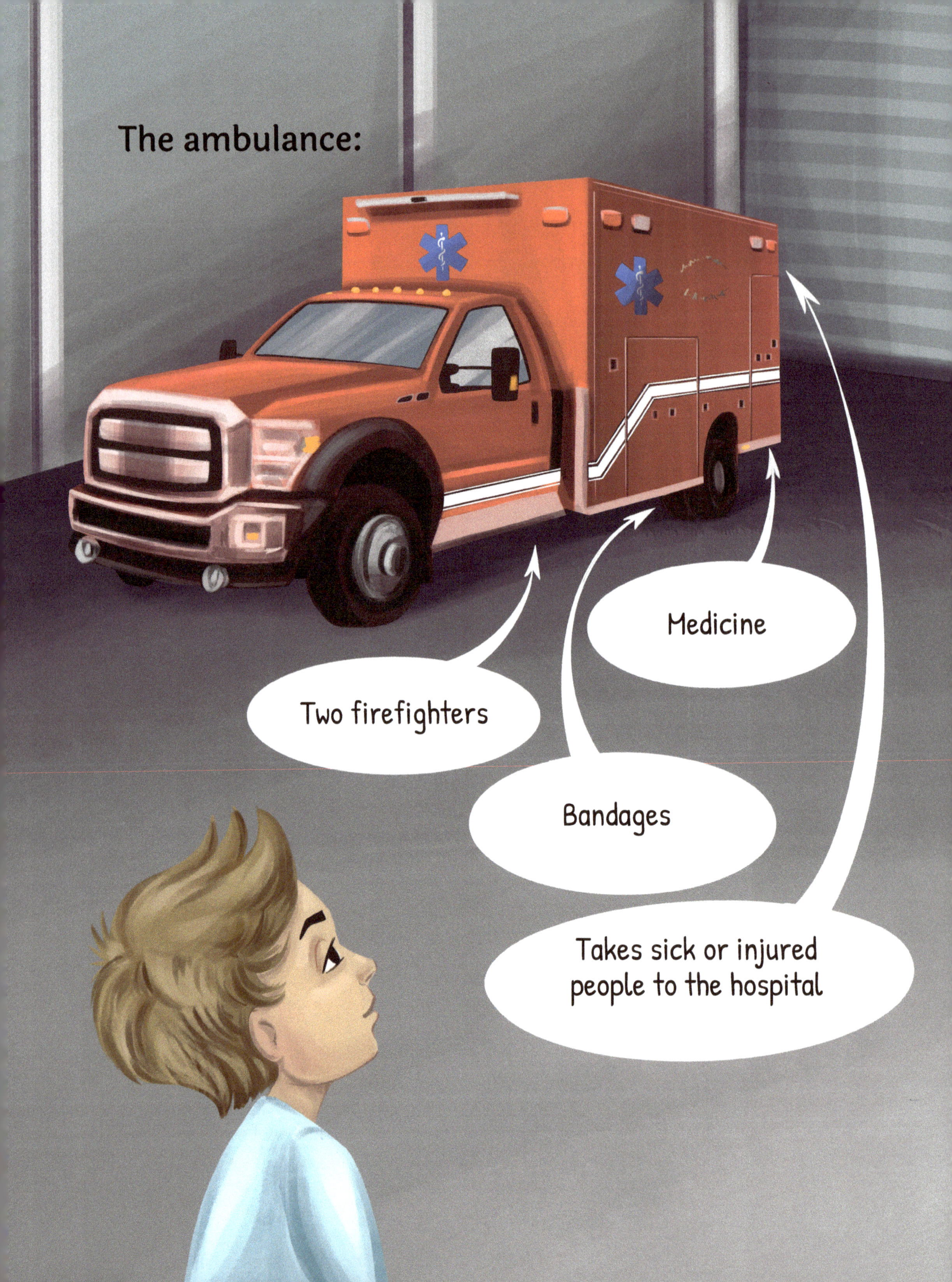
The ambulance:
Two firefighters
Medicine
Bandages
Takes sick or injured people to the hospital

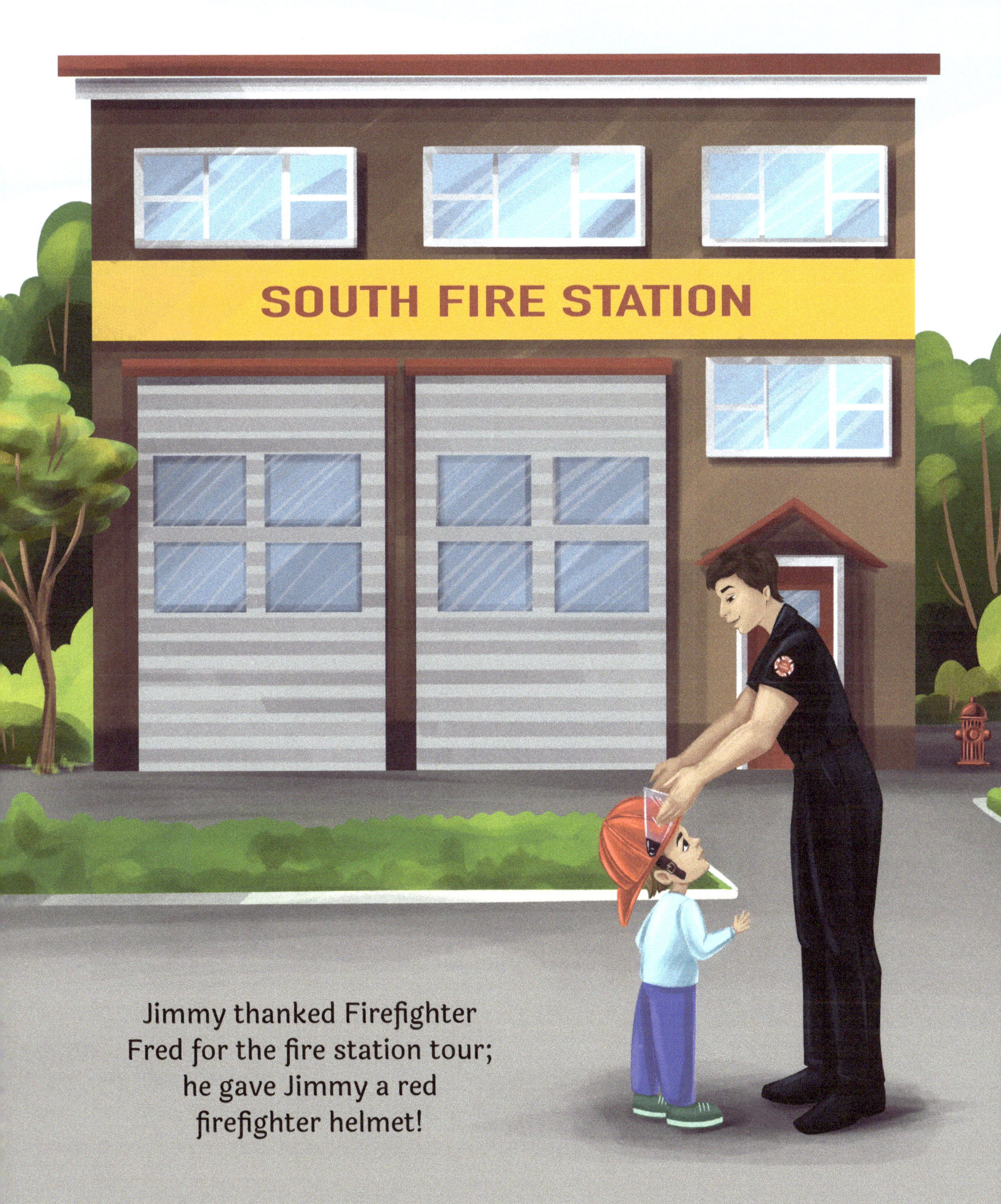

Jimmy thanked Firefighter
Fred for the fire station tour;
he gave Jimmy a red
firefighter helmet!

One day, Jimmy and his friends
went to the park to play.

At the park, Jimmy's friend Mary fell and hurt her leg.
Jimmy remembered what Firefighter Fred taught his class.
He called 9-1-1 for help.

The firefighters arrived in an ambulance
and helped Jimmy's friend Mary.

The next day, Jimmy visited the fire station with his mom
to thank the firefighters who helped his friend.

Jimmy continued to visit the fire station
as he got older.

What do you think
Jimmy is
thinking about?

Jimmy goes to college to learn how to be a firefighter.

Jimmy becomes a firefighter!

One day, Firefighter Fred visited the school and told the class that this would be his last time reading at their school. They would have a new reader the next time a firefighter read to their class.

WHO DO YOU THINK THE NEW READER IS?

Firefighter Jimmy was now the firefighter reading to the kindergartners, just as Firefighter Fred had read to him when he was in kindergarten!

photo by A. Stasch

Author Ron Rakosnik spent over forty years in professional firefighting—his last ten years as a fire chief. Every October, he enjoyed reading stories to preschool and kindergarten classes in his community during Fire Prevention Week. Upon his retirement, he decided to give back to the community he served and protected for many years (and others) by writing this enjoyable, educational, and inspirational book for young citizens.